CONTENTS

HOW THE BOOK IS SET OUT

• There are eighteen different topics.

• Each one is dealt with in a separate unit.

• Each unit has two sections:-
1. The INTRODUCTION with a worked Example and Step by Step instructions.
2. The EXERCISE with some Hints for extra help.

• A detachable answers sheet is provided at the back.

HOW TO USE THIS BOOK

1.   Do the units in order, as they are graded.

2.   Read the INTRODUCTION 2 or 3 times to understand the example.

3.   Do the EXERCISE on your own.

4.   Use the STEP by STEP section and the Hints provided.

5.   If you change an answer, make sure the change is clear.

6.   Each exercise should take between 5 and 10 minutes.

7.   Do not rush!

8.   When you have finished each unit, mark it with an adult.

9.   Enter your score out of 10 at the end of each exercise.

10. Fill in your score on the bar chart on page 44.

A B C D E F G H I J K L M N O P Q R S T U V W X Y Z

Look at these examples.

1. **Which letter appears in the word ORANGE, but <u>not</u> in the word GROAN?** (E)

   The answer is **E**, because   the letters O, R, A, N, and G are in ORAN<u>G</u>E
   and the letters O, R, A, N and G are also in GROAN

   (E appears in ORANGE but not in GROAN)

2. **Which letter occurs <u>twice</u> in PARTICULARLY, <u>but</u> only <u>once</u> in TERRIBLE?** (L)

   The letters A, R and L occur <u>twice</u> in PARTICULARLY

   The answer is **L**, because it appears **twice** in **PARTIC<u>U</u>LAR<u>L</u>Y** and **once** in **TERRIB<u>L</u>E**

   (not A, because there are no A's in the second word)
   (not R, because there are 2 R's in the second word)

STEP BY STEP

THINGS TO LOOK FOR:-

• THE SAME LETTERS APPEARING TWICE IN THE ONE WORD
• TWICE MEANS TWO TIMES

STEP 1:- Read each question carefully 2 or 3 times!

STEP 2:- Mark all the letters that occur in both words..

STEP 3:- Cross out letters that are **not** needed.

STEP 4:- Use the letters that remain to find you answer..

A B C D E F G H I J K L M N O P Q R S T U V W X Y Z

**Write the answers to the following questions in the space provided.
If necessary use the HINTS.**

1 — What is the 16th letter of the alphabet?
Count A as 1, B as 2, C as 3, etc.

(_____)

2 — If the alphabet is written backwards which letter is in the
12th position?
Count Z as 1, Y as 2, X as 3 etc.

(_____)

3 — Which letter appears in RESIDENT, but **not** in REINVEST?

(_____)

4 — Which letter occurs **twice** in INDIA and **twice** in BRITAIN?
Twice means two times.

(_____)

5 — Which letter occurs **once** in FLAG, but **twice** in MELANCHOLY?
Which letter appears twice in the second word?

(_____)

6 — Which letter occurs **twice** in SUPPORTER, but only **once** in OVERTAKE?
There are two letters that are repeated in the first word.

(_____)

7 — Which letter occurs **once** in EXERCISE, but **twice** in SUCCESS?

(_____)

8 — Which letter occurs **twice** as often in POTATOES as it does in SILENT?
Which letter appears twice in the first word but appears only once in the second.

(_____)

9 — Which letter occurs **once** in GINGER, **twice** in BEGINNER but **not**
at all in DIVIDE?
Which letter appears twice in the second word?

(_____)

10 — Which letter occurs **twice** in POMEGRANATE, **twice** in PINEAPPLE,
but only once in PROPERLY?

(_____)

Score 10

UNIT 2 USING LETTERS TO MAKE NEW WORDS

Some letters from the key word in CAPITALS have been used to make other words.
Underline the TWO new words that have been made each time.

Look at this example.

(key word) C O N V E N I E N T   <u>tonic</u>   video   notion   <u>voice</u>

The answers are **tonic** and **voice**,

because the letters of **tonic** are found in   C O N V E N I E N T

and so are those of **voice**.   C O N V E N I E N T

(Not 'video' as there is no D, and not 'notion' because CONVENIENT has only 1 letter 'O'.)

STEP BY STEP

THINGS TO LOOK FOR:-

•UNDERLINE **TWO** ANSWERS EACH TIME (NOT 1, NOT 3, NOT 4!)
• USE EACH LETTER OF THE KEY WORD **ONCE ONLY**.

• WORDS WITH 2 LETTERS THE SAME CAN ONLY BE MADE
IF THE SAME 2 LETTERS ARE **ALSO** IN THE KEY WORD.

STEP 1:- Check the letters of each given word against the key word in capitals.

STEP 2:- Ignore any words that have letters missing from the key word.

STEP 3:- Check carefully that when there are 2 letters the same in the given word
this same letter also appears twice in the key word.

Some letters from the words in CAPITALS have been used to make other words.
Underline the TWO new words that have been made each time.
If necessary use the HINTS.

1 CURTAIN   train   stain   rain   track

In 2 of the given words, there is one letter that does **not** appear in the key word.

2 PREVENT   seven   rent   trip   even

3 SCRATCH   chats   crutch   crate   catch

4 ASSEMBLY   mess   slim   beams   boys

5 HOLIDAYS   diary   daisy   sails   solid

One word cannot be made as it has 2 letters the same <u>not</u> repeated in the key word.

6 LEARNING   angelic   inner   engine   angle

One word cannot be made as it has 2 letters the same <u>not</u> repeated in the key word.

7 TOGETHER   there   rotate   rotter   hotter

8 DANDELION   allied   nailed   linen   noon

Two words cannot be made as each one has 2 letters the same that do not appear in the key word.

9 REASONING   ringer   insane   season   sinner

10 EXAMINATION   notion   imitate   meant   intone

Score 10

A B C D E F G H I J K L M N O P Q R S T U V W X Y Z

Look at this example.

Put these five words in alphabetical order.

angry, afford, acorn, affect, about

The answer is **about, acorn, affect, afford, angry,**

because   **a <u>b</u>** out
           a <u>c</u> orn
           a <u>f f e</u> ct
           a <u>f f o</u> rd
           a <u>n</u> gry

STEP BY STEP

THINGS TO LOOK FOR:-

•WORDS STARTING WITH THE SAME LETTERS
•WORDS WITH MORE THAN ONE LETTER THE SAME AT THE BEGINNING
•LENGTH OF WORDS IS NOT IMPORTANT

STEP 1:-   If the first letters of words are the same,
               sort out the order from their second letters.

STEP 2:-   If the 2nd letters of any words are the same,
               sort out the order from their third letters.

STEP 3:-   If the 3rd letters of any words are the same,
               sort out the order from their fourth letters, etc.,.

A B C D E F G H I J K L M N O P Q R S T U V W X Y Z

Put the five words of each question in alphabetical order. If necessary use the HINTS. The alphabet has been printed to help you.

1 hope, jet, easy, apple, zoo,

(_____) (_____) (_____) (_____) (_____)

2 young, old, pear, king, parrot,

(_____) (_____) (_____) (_____) (_____)

3 ten, tap, toe, tune, tin,
Look at vowels in second position

(_____) (_____) (_____) (_____) (_____)

4 swab, slope, slip, swig, stop,
Look at the 2ⁿᵈ or 3ʳᵈ letter of each word

(_____) (_____) (_____) (_____) (_____)

5 gap, ghost, garage, gannet, grumble,
Look at the 3ʳᵈ letter of the three words starting with ga

(_____) (_____) (_____) (_____) (_____)

6 excuse, execute, exit, exclude, exciting,
Look at the 4ᵗʰ letter of each word starting with exc

(_____) (_____) (_____) (_____) (_____)

7 treble, tree, trend, tremble, treat,

(_____) (_____) (_____) (_____) (_____)

8 profit, prosper, protect, programme, profess,
Look at 4ᵗʰ or 5ᵗʰ letters.

(_____) (_____) (_____) (_____) (_____)

9 shake, shade, shades, shack, shaded,
If all letters at the beginning are the same, the shortest word comes first.

(_____) (_____) (_____) (_____) (_____)

10 flag, fleece, fleeting, flake, fleet,
Look at 3ʳᵈ, 4ᵗʰ, 5ᵗʰ or 6ᵗʰ letters.

(_____) (_____) (_____) (_____) (_____)

Score 10

UNIT 4   MAKE SENSE OF SENTENCES

Underline the TWO WORDS in each sentence that must CHANGE PLACES so that the sentence makes sense.

Look at these examples.

1.   **The <u>wood</u> was made of <u>table.</u>**

The answers are <u>**wood**</u> and <u>**table**</u> because when they CHANGE PLACES
the sentence makes sense. Say it out loud to check!

2.   **<u>Your</u> driving <u>you're</u> car very fast.**

The answers are <u>**your**</u> and <u>**you're**</u> because these two words that sound the same have been mixed up.

STEP BY STEP

THINGS TO LOOK FOR:-

- QUESTIONS AND ORDINARY SENTENCES THAT ARE MIXED UP
- WORDS SOUNDING THE SAME THAT ARE MIXED UP

STEP 1:-   By saying the sentence out loud, find which part does not make sense.

STEP 2:-   Find one of the words out of place.

STEP 3:-   Ask yourself what it could be and find this word in the sentence.

STEP 4:-   Swop over the two chosen words and check that it now makes sense.

Underline the TWO WORDS in each sentence that must CHANGE PLACES so that the sentence makes sense. If necessary, use the HINTS.

1 Next week be will I in France.

2 Do not last your homework until the leave moment!

3 The the on rug floor is dirty.

4 Who it was outside the door?

5 That is your friend Robert?
Make it a proper question.

6 They say can money make you happy.
This is <u>not</u> supposed to be a question.

7 You was the only person who were here.
Look at the two forms of the verb, "to be"

8 There are for presents four you.
Look at words that sound the same.

9 The cat was to ill too eat.

10 The subtraction from 3 of 5 gives the answer 2.
It is <u>not</u> any of the numbers that change places.

Score 10

JUMBLED WORDS

In the following questions the letters of words have been jumbled up.
Find the word each time. Clues are given to help you.

Look at these examples.

1.	**IATSDUM**	Sports Ground	**STADIUM**
2.	**NOBRI**	A type of bird	**ROBIN**
3.	**VESEN**	A number	**SEVEN**
4.	**KBOO**	Contains stories	**BOOK**

STEP BY STEP

THINGS TO LOOK FOR:-

• ALL THE LETTERS OF THE JUMBLED WORD MUST BE USED IN YOUR ANSWER.
•DO NOT PUT IN ANY EXTRA LETTERS THAT ARE NOT GIVEN IN THE JUMBLED WORD.
•LEAVE ANY QUESTION THAT YOU CANNOT DO AND COME BACK TO IT AT THE END.

STEP 1:-   Think of words suggested by the hint.

STEP 2:-   Match one of them to the jumbled letters given.

STEP 3:-   Cross out all the given jumbled letters as you use each one for the answer.

STEP 4:-   Check the spelling of your final answer.

In the following questions the letters of the words have been jumbled up. Find the word each time. If necessary use the HINTS.

1   U P J M   Leap over   (_____)

2   F O A S   Something to sit on   (_____)

3   R O H U   A measure of time   (_____)

4   C W I E T   Double or 2 times   (_____)

5   R E L G A   Big, but not enormous   (_____)

6   T R Y F O   A number with 4 in it   (_____)

7   T E N L A P   What the Earth is   (_____)

8   N E G O L U   The room at home for watching TV   (_____)

9   T H E P A R N   One of the big cat family   (_____)

10   O R M T O R W O   The next day   (_____)

Score 10

Give the next letter in each series. The alphabet is printed to help you.

A B C D E F G H I J K L M N O P Q R S T U V W X Y Z

Look at these examples.

1.   B, D, F, H, J , ..**L**...,

The answer is **L**, because the pattern is to count forwards in twos from the first given letter.

B   CD   EF   GH   IJ, and now K L

2.   Z, Y, W, T, P, .**K**...,

The answer is **K,** because the pattern is to count backwards from the first given letter:-
first one, then two, then three, then four, and lastly five.

KLMNO   PQRS   TUV   WX   YZ

STEP BY STEP

THINGS TO LOOK FOR:-

• USE THE PRINTED ALPHABET TO FIND EACH PATTERN
• CHECK YOU ARE CONTINUING EACH PATTERN CORRECTLY
• BE CAREFUL WITH MIXED PATTERNS (LIKE EXAMPLE 2)

STEP 1:-   Look to see if the series is going forwards or backwards.

STEP 2:-   Mark the patterns on the alphabet, as in the two examples above.

STEP 3:-   Check the pattern.

STEP 4:-   Continue the pattern correctly to find the next letter in the series.

A B C D E F G H I J K L M N O P Q R S T U V W X Y Z

Give the next letter in each series. The alphabet is printed to help you.
If necessary, use the HINTS.

1 C, D, E, F, G, (____)
Going forwards!

2 A, D, G, J, M, (____)
Count forwards in threes.

3 J, L, M, O, P, (____)
Count forwards in twos and ones, each in turn.

4 D, E, H, I, L, M, (____)
Count forwards in ones and threes, each in turn.

5 X, W, V, U, T, (____)
Going backwards!

6 X, W, U, T, R, Q, (____)
Count backwards in ones and twos, each in turn.

7 F, G, I, L, P, (____)
Count forwards one, then two, then three, then four, then (?).

8 W, V, T, Q, M, (____)
Like the pattern in question 7, but going backwards.

9 A, B, E, J, Q, (____)
Count forwards one, then three, then five, then seven, then (?).

10 Z, Y, V, Q, J, (____)
Like the pattern in question 9, but going backwards.

Score **10**

MAKING ONE WORD FROM TWO
(COMPOUNDS)

Underline TWO words, one from each side, which together make ONE new word, spelt correctly.

The word on the left always comes first.

Look at these examples:

1. **<u>BLACK</u>**   ALL   TOP   OVER   **<u>BIRD</u>**   TOY

    The answers are **<u>BLACK</u>** and **<u>BIRD</u>,**
    because when joined together, in that order, these two words make a new word: **BLACKBIRD**
    (<u>Not</u>   OVER and ALL because the word on the left must come first)

2. CORN   **<u>FARM</u>**   TIME   OR   FIELD   **<u>YARD</u>**

    The answers are **<u>FARM</u>** and **<u>YARD</u>,**
    because when joined together they make a new word: **FARMYARD**
    (Not FARM and OR because the word FARMER is spelt with <u>ER</u> at the end)

STEP BY STEP

THINGS TO LOOK FOR:-

- COMMON BEGINNINGS LIKE '**BLACK-**', '**HOUSE-**', '**IN-**', etc.
- COMMON ENDINGS LIKE '**-AGE**', '**-HOOD**', '**-LAND**', etc.
- THE NEW COMPOUND WORD SOMETIMES HAS <u>NO</u> CONNECTION WITH THE TWO WORDS USED (e.g. **BE AT** gives **<u>BEAT</u>**)
- THE WORD ON THE LEFT <u>ALWAYS</u> COMES FIRST - (THE OTHER WAY ROUND IS <u>NOT</u> ALLOWED!)

STEP 1:-   Try the 1st word in the left hand group with each of the words in the right hand group.

STEP 2:-   If this doesn't give an answer, repeat the process using the 2nd word in the left hand group.

STEP 3:-   If this doesn't give an answer, repeat the process using the 3rd word in the left hand group.

STEP 4:-   Make sure your chosen answer is spelt correctly!

In each line below a word from the left-hand group joins with a word from the right-hand group to make ONE new word. The left-hand word always comes first.

Underline the chosen words. If necessary use the HINTS.

1
BLACK   VERY   TO   BORED   BOARD   MEET
Check your spelling!

2
DIRT   MILE   HOUSE   WIFE   HOPE   GO
Remember one of the common beginnings.

3
HER   IN   SO   OUT   BAR   TEND
The two words joined together must make a new word.

4
GRASS   TREE   POST   PAT   AGE   GREEN
Remember one of the common endings.

5
BALL   IS   ASH   OR   GOT   LAND
The word is not pronounced as it is written!

6
CHILD   LIE   GOAT   GRAND   HOOD   MAN
Start always with one word from the left-hand group.

7
MISS   OVER   TIME   TAKE   LIE   LIFE
Check your spelling, or you will get this one wrong!

8
MY   HE   UP   AT   IN   NO
The new word has no connection with the two old ones.

9
BE   AT   SO   DO   ME   IF
Check the spelling of your answer.

10
CUT   PUT   GROW   WING   TEN   LED
Be very careful that your answer is spelt correctly!

Score 10

Give the next <u>pair</u> of letters in each series, in order to complete the sequence.
The alphabet is printed to help you.

$$\text{A B C D E F G H I J K L M N O P Q R S T U V W X Y Z}$$

Look at these examples.

1. A H, B I, C J, D K, (<u>EL</u>)

The answer is **E L**, because the pattern is to count forwards in ones for both the first letter
and the second letter:

first letter	**AH**	**BI**	**CJ**	**DK**	<u>**E**</u>
second letter	**AH**	**BI**	**CJ**	**DK**	E<u>**L**</u>

2. F A, E C, D E, C G, (<u>BI</u>)

The answer is **B I**, because the pattern is to count backwards in ones for the first letter, and count forwards
in twos for the second letter.

first letter	**FA**	**EC**	**DE**	**CG**	<u>**B**</u>
second letter	**FA**	**EC**	**DE**	**CG**	B<u>**I**</u>

STEP BY STEP

THINGS TO LOOK FOR:-

• EACH SERIES HAS TWO SEPARATE PATTERNS.
• THE FIRST LETTER FOLLOWS ONE PATTERN, THE SECOND USUALLY FOLLOWS
A DIFFERENT PATTERN.
• BE CAREFUL NOT TO MIX UP THE TWO PATTERNS.

STEP 1:-   By counting forwards or backwards, work out the pattern for the first letter in each series.

STEP 2:-   Continue this pattern correctly to find the first letter.

STEP 3:-   Work out and continue the pattern for the second letter.

STEP 4:-   Mark the patterns on the alphabet as in the two examples above.

Give the next pair of letters in each series in order to complete the sequence.
The alphabet is printed to help you. If necessary use the HINTS.

1   A V,   B W,   C X,   D Y,   (___EZ___)
Going forwards on both.

2   E Z,   D Y,   C X,   B W,   (___AV___)
Going backwards on both.

3   F A,   G C,   H E,   I G,   (___JI___)
Going forwards on the first letter, count forwards in twos for the second.

4   Z W,   X U,   V S,   T Q,   (___RO___)
Count backwards in twos for both the first and second letters.

5   L T,   M R,   N P,   O N,   (___PL___)
Going forwards on the first letter, count backwards in twos for the second.

6   Y B,   X D,   W F,   V H,   (___UJ___)
Going backwards on the first, count forwards in twos for the second.

7   A J,   D K,   G L,   J M,   (___MN___)
Count forwards in threes for the first, going forwards on the second.

8   B I,   E K,   H M,   K O,   (___NQ___)
Count forwards in threes for the first, but in twos for the second.

9   X O,   W L,   V I,   U F,   (___TC___)
Going backwards on the first, count backwards in threes for the second.

10   N W,   K T,   H Q,   E N,   (___BK___)
Count backwards in threes for both the first and second letters.

Score 10

Find the words that the following codes stand for.

Look at these examples.

In a certain code T E A C H I N G is written as V G C E J K P I

1. **What word does E J K P C stand for?**

   The answer is **C H I N A** because **E J K P C** stands for these letters as shown by the grid below, when reading from the code line downwards↓.

(Code)	V	G	C	E	J	K	P	I
(Word)	T	E	A	C	H	I	N	G

In another code B E L T is written as M R I C and S U M is written as T B A

2. **What word does T I B A stand for?**

   The answer is **S L U M** because **T I B A** stands for these letters as shown by the grid below, when reading from the code line downwards↓.

(Code)	M	R	I	C		T	B	A
(Word)	B	E	L	T		S	U	M

STEP BY STEP

THINGS TO LOOK FOR:-

• TO FIND THE WORD WRITE THE CODE ON THE TOP LINE OF THE GRID.
• ALWAYS READ FROM THE TOP LINE DOWNWARDS ↓ TO FIND THE ANSWER.

STEP 1:- Write the code on the top line of the grid.

STEP 2:- Write the keyword on the bottom line of the grid.

STEP 3:- Find the word by reading from the top line of the grid downwards ↓.

In a certain code P E N C I L is written as B D F K J S .

What words do these codes stand for? If necessary, use the HINTS.

(Code)	. . . .	. . . .	. . . .	. . . .	. . . .	. . . .
(Word)	. . . .	. . . .	. . . .	. . . .	. . . .	. . . .

1   **B J F D**   (_____)

First fill in the grid above, then read from the top downwards ↓.

2   **K S J B**   (_____)

Always read from the top line downwards ↓.

In a certain code P O L A R   B E A R is written as S R O D U   E H D U .

What words do these codes stand for? If necessary, use the HINTS.

(Code)	. . . .	. . . .	. . . .	. . . .	. . . .	▓	. . . .	. . . .	. . . .	. . . .
(Word)	. . . .	. . . .	. . . .	. . . .	. . . .	▓	. . . .	. . . .	. . . .	. . . .

3   **U R O O**   (_____)

Remeber to fill in the grid and read from the top downwards ↓.

4   **S H D U O**   (_____)

5   **U R E E H U**   (_____)

(This unit continues on the next page)

SIMPLE LETTER CODES
(PUT WORDS INTO CODE)

Put into code the following words.

Look at these examples.

In a certain code T E A C H I N G   is written as   V G C E J K P I.

Put the word C H A T into code.

The answer is **E J C V** because these are the code letters for **C H A T**
as shown by the grid below, when reading from the word line downwards↓.

(Word)	T	E	A	C	H	I	N	G
(Code)	V	G	C	E	J	K	P	I

In another code B E L T is written as M R I C and S U M is written as T B A.

Put the word S M E L T into code.

The answer is   **T A R I C**   because these are the code letters for   **S M E L T**
as shown by the grid below, when reading from the word line downwards↓.

(Word)	B	E	L	T		S	U	M
(Code)	M	R	I	C		T	B	A

STEP BY STEP

THINGS TO LOOK FOR:-

- TO PUT INTO CODE, WRITE THE KEY WORD(S) ON THE TOP LINE OF THE GRID.
- ALWAYS READ FROM THE TOP LINE DOWNWARDS ↓ TO FIND THE ANSWER.

STEP 1:-   Write the key word on the top line of the grid.

STEP 2:-   Write the complete code on the bottom line of the grid.

STEP 3:-   Put into code by reading from the top line downwards ↓.

In a certain code L E A R N I N G is written as I Y L M G X G P

Put the following words into code.

(Word)	. . . .	. . . .	. . . .	. . . .	. . . .	. . . .	. . . .	. . . .
(Code)	. . . .	. . . .	. . . .	. . . .	. . . .	. . . .	. . . .	. . . .

6 **G R A I N**   (_____)

First fill in the grid above, then read from the top downwards ↓.

7 **A N G L E**   (_____)

In a certain code Z E B R A is written as C H E U D
H O R S E is written as K R U V H .

Put the following words into code.

(Words)	. . . .	. . . .	. . . .	. . . .	. . . .	▓	. . . .	. . . .	. . . .	. . . .	. . . .
(Codes)	. . . .	. . . .	. . . .	. . . .	. . . .	▓	. . . .	. . . .	. . . .	. . . .	. . . .

8 **Z O O S**   (_____)

First fill in the grid above, then read from the top downwards ↓.

9 **B E A R**   (_____)

10 **S H A R E**   (_____)

The first word can be changed into the last word by replacing one letter at a time and each time making a proper word spelt correctly. Find the missing word.

Look at these examples.

1.   T I D E   (**RIDE**   )   R O D E

The answer is **R I D E** because when **T** is replaced by **R** , this makes a word.
(Not I but O as 'TODE' is not a word.)

The example is easier to understand if the words are set out below each other like this:-

```
        T I D E                    T I D E
                                      ↓
(_____)            (   R I D E   )          (Stage 1)
                                      ↓
        R O D E                    R O D E          (Stage 2)
```

The arrows show how one letter is being replaced each time to make a proper word spelt correctly.

2.   L O S E   (**LOST**   )   L A S T

The answer is **L O S T** because when **E** is replaced by **T** , this makes a word.
(Not O but A, as 'LASE' is not a word.)

```
        L O S E                    L O S E
                                      ↓
(_____)            (   L O S T   )          (Stage 1)
                                      ↓
        L A S T                    L A S T          (Stage 2)
```

STEP BY STEP

THINGS TO LOOK FOR :-

• YOUR ANSWERS SHOULD BE SPELT CORRECTLY
• MAKE SURE THAT ONLY <u>ONE</u> LETTER FROM THE FIRST WORD
HAS BEEN CHANGED IN EACH STEP

STEP 1:-   Find the two letters in the first word that are different in the last word.

STEP 2:-   Replace one letter of the first word with the corresponding letter from the last word.

STEP 3:-   If necessary, replace the other letter of the first word with its
corresponding letter from the last word.

STEP 4:-   Check that your answer has three letters of the first word that are still
the same and is a proper word spelt correctly.

The first word can be changed into the last word in two stages, by replacing one letter at a time and each time making a proper word spelt correctly. Find the missing word. If necessary use the HINTS.

1   T A K E   (_____)   L I K E
Replace the first letter.

2   R E N T   (_____)   T I N T

3   H E A T   (_____)   B O A T

4   C H I N   (_____)   T H E N

5   H E R E   (_____)   H A V E
Replace the second letter.

6   B U R N   (_____)   B O R E

7   C O A T   (_____)   C O S Y
Replace the third letter.

8   S O L D   (_____)   S A L E
Replace the fourth letter.

9   P A N E   (_____)   P I N T
Careful with spelling!

10   F O U R   (_____)   F O O L

Score **10**

UNIT 11 USING LETTERS FOR NUMBERS

In the following questions letters take the place of numbers. Complete each of the sums and give the answers as LETTERS.

Look at these examples.

1. If A = 7   B = 2   C = 4   D = 1   then

$$2 + 4 + 1 = \qquad 7$$
$$B + C + D = \qquad (\underline{A})$$

2. If A = 4   B = 3   C = 20   D = 15   then

$$15 \div 3 \; x \; 4 = \qquad 20$$
$$D \div B \; x \; A = \qquad (\underline{C})$$

STEP BY STEP

THINGS TO LOOK FOR:-

• USE THE GIVEN NUMBERS FOR A, B, C, D and E.

• ONLY THE GIVEN LETTERS MAY BE USED (DO NOT MAKE NEW ONES!)

• DO THE CORRECT SUMS EACH TIME

• IF YOUR FINAL ANSWER IS NOT ONE OF THE GIVEN LETTERS CHECK YOUR WORKING OUT

STEP 1:-   Write the value of each letter above that letter in the sum.

STEP 2:-   Work out the answer to the sum.

STEP 3:-   Write your final answer as a letter.

In the following questions letters take the place of numbers. Complete each of the sums and give the answers as LETTERS. If necessary use the HINTS.

LETTER

1 If $A = 1$ $B = 3$ $C = 5$ $D = 9$ then $A + B + C =$ (_____)

$A + B =$ .... $+ C =$ .... Then write the answer as a LETTER.

2 If $A = 3$ $B = 10$ $C = 7$ $D = 14$ then $D - C + A =$ (_____)

$D - C =$ .... $+ A =$ .... Then write the answer as a LETTER.

3 If $A = 9$ $B = 6$ $C = 15$ $D = 3$ then $C - A - D =$ (_____)

Do the correct sum each time!

4 If $A = 7$ $B = 8$ $C = 14$ $D = 15$ then $A + D - B =$ (_____)

$A + D =$ .... $- B =$ ....

5 If $A = 20$ $B = 16$ $C = 6$ $D = 2$ then $A - C + D =$ (_____)

Write the answer as a LETTER!

6 If $A = 5$ $B = 6$ $C = 9$ $D = 8$ then $A + C - B =$ (_____)

$A + C =$ .... $- B =$ ....

7 If $A = 8$ $B = 12$ $C = 24$ $D = 4$ then $C \div A \times D =$ (_____)

$C \div A =$ .... $\times D =$ ....

8 If $A = 5$ $B = 4$ $C = 9$ $D = 11$ then $A \times B - D =$ (_____)

$A \times B =$ .... $- D =$ ....

9 If $A = 4$ $B = 5$ $C = 11$ $D = 18$ $E = 10$ then $E \div B \times C - D =$ (_____)

$E \div B =$ .... $\times C =$ .... $- D =$ ....

10 If $A = 4$ $B = 3$ $C = 7$ $D = 6$ $E = 5$ then $D \times D \div A - B =$ (_____)

Score 10

Move one letter from the first word and place it into the second word to make
TWO NEW WORDS spelt correctly.

Write the letter moved and both NEW words.

Look at this example.

	The letter moved is:-	The answer is:-
THEN TANK	**H**	(**TEN**) (**THANK**)

H moves from the first word **THEN** to leave the new word **TEN**
and is placed into the second word to make another new word **THANK**.

STEP BY STEP

THINGS TO LOOK FOR:-

• ALWAYS MOVE THE LETTER FROM THE FIRST WORD (NOT THE SECOND)
• ONLY MOVE **ONE** LETTER (NOT TWO)
• ALL THE OTHER LETTERS MUST STAY IN THE SAME ORDER
• TRY MOVING THE LETTER INTO ANY POSITION IN THE SECOND WORD:
BEFORE THE FIRST LETTER, BEFORE THE SECOND, ETC.

STEP 1:-   Move each letter in turn from the first word until you are left with a new word.

STEP 2:-   Put the letter you took away into the second word, trying each place in turn.

STEP 3:-   Repeat Steps 1 and 2 until you find **another** new word.

STEP 4:-   Write down the letter you moved and then the **two new words.**

Move one letter from the first word and place it into the second word to make TWO NEW WORDS spelt correctly.

Write the letter moved and both NEW words. If necessary, use the HINTS.

		Letter moved	Answer	

1   M A N   F O R   ____   (_____)   (_____)

2   W E T   E A R   ____   (_____)   (_____)

3   T I M E   Z O O   ____   (_____)   (_____)

4   C O A T   F I R   ____   (_____)   (_____)
Only one letter when moved makes a new second word.

5   T W I N   H E A R   (_____)   (_____)
The new second word is pronounced differently.

6   B A B Y   P L U M   (_____)   (_____)
One new word has a 'silent' letter.

7   S T A R E   H O P   ____   (_____)   (_____)
Check your spelling !

8   B R A N D   C O W   ____   (_____)   (_____)

9   R E A C H   P I C K   ____   (_____)   (_____)

10   H O A R D   H E L L   ____   (_____)   (_____)
Not easy this one !

Score 10

In each line below write, in the brackets, one letter which completes both the word in front of the brackets and the word after the brackets.

Look at this example.

R O P (__E__) V E R

The answer is **E** because it completes the first word ROPE and also begins the second word EVER.

STEP BY STEP

THINGS TO LOOK FOR:-

• GO THROUGH THE ALPHABET LETTER BY LETTER
• BOTH NEW WORDS MUST BE SPELT CORRECTLY

STEP 1:- Find a letter that completes the first word by going through the alphabet.

STEP 2:- Check that this letter also completes the second word.

STEP 3:- Repeat Steps 1 and 2 until you find one letter that completes both words.

STEP 4:- Make sure both new words are spelt correctly.

A B C D E F G H I J K L M N O P Q R S T U V W X Y Z

In each line below write, in the brackets, one letter which completes both the word in front of the brackets and the word after the brackets. If necessary, use the HINTS.

1 E Y (_____) A R

Remember the vowels.

2 S K (_____) C E

3 B E (_____) A S

Go through the alphabet.

4 B O T (_____) U R T

5 M A N (_____) A R D

Near the end of the alphabet.

6 S E A (_____) U R N

Check the spelling of the second word!

7 B E A (_____) I T E

Remember which words end in -ight.

8 S H A R (_____) R I N T

9 C A M E (_____) I G H T

The first word is an animal.

10 B A R R O (_____) E I G H T

Wheel it!

Score **10**

A FOUR letter word is hidden between TWO WORDS that are next to each other in each of the sentences below. Every hidden word can be found by studying the letters at the end of one word and the letters at the beginning of the next word.

Write the hidden word in the brackets. It must be a proper word that is spelt correctly.

Look at these examples.

1.   **Time and tide wait for no man.**   (__MEAN__)

The answer is **M E A N** because this is hidden between the two words '**Ti**me **an**d'.

The last 2 letters of '**Time**' and the first 2 letters of '**and**' form the hidden word, as shown by the underlining.

2.   **We must welcome the new boy.**   (__THEN__)

The answer is **T H E N** because this is hidden between the two words '**the new**'.

All 3 letters of '**the**' and the first letter of '**new**' form the hidden word, as shown by the underlining.

(Not 'come', as this is hidden in one word, instead of between TWO words)

STEP BY STEP

THINGS TO LOOK FOR:-

• THE WORD IS ALWAYS HIDDEN BETWEEN **TWO WORDS THAT ARE NEXT TO EACH OTHER**
• THE HIDDEN WORD ALWAYS HAS 4 LETTERS   (NOT 3, NOT 5 !)
• THE LETTERS ALWAYS **STAY IN THE SAME ORDER** AS THEY APPEAR IN THE SENTENCE

STEP 1:-   Go from left to right along each sentence taking 2 words at a time.

STEP 2:-   Each time put the **last 3** letters of the first word with the **first letter** of the second word.
If you do not get an answer go to Step 3.

STEP 3:-   Put the **last 2** letters of the first word with the **first 2** letters of the second word.
If you do not get an answer go to Step 4.

STEP 4:-   Put the **last** letter of the first word with the **first 3** letters of the second word.
If you have not found the hidden word go back to step 1.

A FOUR letter word is hidden between TWO WORDS that are next to each other in each of the sentences below. Every hidden word can be found by studying the letters at the end of one word and the letters at the beginning of the next word.

Write the hidden word in the brackets. It must be a proper word that is spelt correctly. **If necessary, use the HINTS.**

1 This is an easy exercise at first.   (_____)
Use the last 2 letters of one word, and the first 2 of the next.

2 It will then start to get harder.   (_____)
Use the last 3 letters of one word, and the first 1 of the next.

3 Reasoning books are still great fun.   (_____)
The word is hidden between 2 words next to each other (not in one word).

4 The best way of all is Learning Together.   (_____)
Use the last letter of one word, and the first 3 letters of the next.

5 Some always do it this way.   (_____)
Use the last 2 letters of one word and the first 2 of the next.

6 For my birthday I want more tests.   (_____)
The word is hidden right at the beginning!

7 It is well hidden this word.   (_____)
The hidden word always has 4 letters, not 5.

8 If you are clever you can make a word.   (_____)
Clever you, if you find the hidden word!

9 Nobody gets bored with eating.   (_____)

10 How glad we are this test is over!   (_____)

Score 10

The information below is about 4 children, John, Katie, Lucy and Mike and the flavours of fruit juices they like.

John and Katie are the only two who like both apple and orange.
Katie and Mike are the only two who like both orange and blackcurrant.
Lucy and John are the only two who like both grapefruit and cranberry.

A grid has been drawn to show the information,
using the initials of the 4 children.
The box has been <u>ticked</u> ✓ for each flavour that
the child <u>likes</u>.
The box is left <u>empty</u> ☐ for each flavour that the
child does <u>not</u> like.

	J	K	L	M
Apple	✓	✓		
Orange	✓	✓		✓
Blackcurrant		✓		✓
Grapefruit	✓		✓	
Cranberry	✓		✓	

1.   **Who likes orange, but <u>not</u> blackcurrant juice?**   (__John__)
      The answer is **John** because, in the grid only John has <u>both</u> the 'orange box' ticked ✓
      <u>and</u> the blackcurrant box 'empty', ☐ .

2.   **Who likes orange, blackcurrant and apple?**   (__Katie__)
      The answer is **Katie** because, in the grid <u>only</u> Katie has <u>these three</u> flavours ticked ✓.

STEP BY STEP

THINGS TO LOOK FOR:-

• IF GIVEN THE CHILDREN THAT DO <u>NOT</u> LIKE IT, ALWAYS PUT A TICK ✓ IN THE GRID
FOR THE <u>OTHERS</u> THAT <u>DO</u>.
•BE CAREFUL WITH WORDS LIKE '**EXCEPT**' AND '**ALL BUT**' WHICH MEAN '**<u>NOT</u>**'.
• QUESTIONS WITH '**HOW MANY?**' HAVE A NUMBER AS THE ANSWER

STEP 1:-   Write the initials of the children on the top row of the grid.

STEP 2:-   Write each subject heading in the left hand column.

STEP 3:-   Put a tick ✓ in the box for each one the child does like.

STEP 4:-   Read off from the completed grid to find each answer.

Aman, Bill, Charlotte, Diana and Eddie are five children at the same school.
Bill and Aman like English, but the others do not.
Aman and Charlotte are the only ones who do <u>not</u> like Maths.
All like Science, except Bill and Eddie.

	....	....	....	....	....
....					
....					
....					

Complete the grid and work out the answers to the following questions. If necessary, use the HINTS.

1 Who likes English but does <u>not</u> like Maths? (_____)
The two children that do <u>not</u> like Maths should have an empty box in the grid.

2 Who does <u>not</u> like English and also does <u>not</u> like Science? (_____)
The two that do <u>not</u> like Science should have an empty box in the grid.

3 Who likes English, but does <u>not</u> like Science? (_____)

4 <u>How many</u> children who like English <u>also</u> like Maths? (_____)
Give the answer as a number.

5 Which child who likes Science <u>also</u> likes Maths? (_____)

There are five friends, Susan, Robert, Bijay, Ashley and Nishma.
Robert and Ashley like football, but the others like tennis.
Only Nishma, Robert and Susan like going abroad for their holidays.
All <u>but</u> Ashley and Bijay have piano lessons.

	....	....	....	....	....
....					
....					
....					
....					

Complete the grid, then work out the answers to the following questions. If necessary, use the HINTS.

6 Who likes football and <u>also</u> likes going abroad for their holidays? (_____)
Find the child who has a box ticked ✓ for both on the grid..

7 Who likes football but does <u>not</u> have piano lessons? (_____)
The two that do <u>not</u> have piano lessons should have an empty box on the grid.

8 Who likes tennis but does <u>not</u> have piano lessons? (_____)

9 <u>How many</u> children who like tennis <u>also</u> have piano lessons? (_____)
Give the answer as a number.

10 <u>How many</u> children who like going abroad do <u>not</u> have piano lessons? (_____)

Score **10**

MATCHING PAIRS
(ANALOGIES)

Match the second pair of words in the same way as the first pair. Underline the correct word in the brackets.

Look at these examples.

1.   **Up is to down as come is to (start, go, after)**

   The answer is **go** because:-

   in the first pair **down** is the opposite of **up** and **go** is the opposite of **come**.

2.   **Monday is to Sunday as Saturday is to (Sunday, Friday, Monday)**

   The answer is **Friday** because:-

   in the first pair **Sunday** is one day before **Monday** and **Friday** is one day before **Saturday**.

STEP BY STEP

THINGS TO LOOK FOR: -

• DO NOT MIX UP '**OPPOSITES**' AND '**SIMILARS**'.
• BE CAREFUL WITH WORDS THAT SOUND THE SAME .

STEP 1:-   Find the connection between the first pair of words.

STEP 2:-   Connect the second pair in the same way.

STEP 3:-   Underline the <u>ONE</u> correct answer.

Match the second pair of words in the same way as the first pair.
Underline the correct word in the brackets. If necessary use the HINTS.

1 **Right** is to **wrong** as **laugh** is to   (shout, weep, chuckle)
Opposite meanings

2 **Talk** is to **speak** as **listen** is to   (hear, here, shout)
Same meanings

3 **Fox** is to **cub** as **goat** is to   (calf, child, kid)
Adult and baby animals

4 **Arm** is to **body** as **branch** is to   (leaf, tree, trunk)

5 **Me** is to **my** as **them** is to   (they're, there, their)
Different forms of one word

6 **Tuesday** is to **Thursday** as **Monday** is   (Wednesday, Tuesday, Saturday)
Two days <u>after</u>

7 **June** is to **April** as **November** is to   (December, October, September)
Two months <u>before</u>

8 **Wrist** is to **hand** as **ankle** is to   (foot, yard, leg)

9 **Birds** are to **flock** as **fish** are to   (school, shoal, water)
Their 'group' word

10 **Trap** is to **part** as **evil** is to   (live, piece, snare)
Same word spelt backwards

Score 10

In each of the following sentences the word in CAPITALS has 3 letters missing. The missing letters are next to each other. When written in the same order, they make a word on their own.
Write the missing 3 letter words in the brackets.

Look at these examples:

1.   **Begin sentences with CAAL letters.**   (__PIT__)

The answer is **PIT**, because the complete word is CA**PIT**AL
and the 3 missing letters are   **PIT**

2.   **The cat jumped up and STED to run.**   (__ART__)

The answer is **ART**, because the complete word is ST**ART**ED
and the 3 missing letters are   **ART**

STEP BY STEP

THINGS TO LOOK FOR:-

• 3 LETTERS MISSING EACH TIME. (Not 2! Not 4!)
• CHECK YOUR SPELLING OF THE COMPLETED WORD.
• DO <u>NOT</u> CHANGE THE ORDER OF THE LETTERS.
• CHECK YOUR SPELLING OF THE 3 LETTER WORD ANSWER.

STEP 1:-   Read the sentence carefully in order to help you find the missing word.

STEP 2:-   Write down the complete word.

STEP 3:-   Cross out, in the completed word, all the letters already given in capitals in the sentence.

STEP 4:-   Write down the 3 remaining letters as your answer.

In each of the following sentences the word in CAPITALS has 3 letters missing. The missing letters are next to each other and, when written in the same order, they make a word on their own. Write the missing 3 letter words in the brackets. If necessary, use the HINTS.

1 The passengers were waiting on the **PLATM** for the next train. (_____)
There are always 3 letters missing.

2 The driver drove **FORDS** very slowly because of the heavy traffic. (_____)
The three missing letters always make a word.

3 Lee had a big **BOON** outside the house for his birthday. (_____)
There are always 3 missing letters (not 2!).

4 Not one person recognised Claire, as she had **GN** so much taller. (_____)
The 3 missing letters are in the middle.

5 Mum and Dad have gone **SPING** in the local supermarket. (_____)
Check your spelling.

6 After a fierce argument, the two boys started **FIGHG** each other. (_____)

7 Anika must be **CLR** as she got top marks in the test. (_____)

8 The holiday **APARTTS** were near the beach. (_____)
The complete word means 'flats' where people are staying.

9 The girl looked in her purse and found no money, **HING** at all! (_____)
The 3 missing letters are right at the beginning.

10 The doctor said he was ready to see the next **PANT**. (_____)
Careful with spelling!

Score **10**

UNIT 18   FIND A CERTAIN NUMBER

In the following questions you are asked to find the value of a certain number from information given. Find the answer by writing each question in numbers.
Use an empty box ☐ to stand for the missing number.

Look at these examples.

1.   **When 4 is subtracted from a number it gives the answer 16.**

   What is the number?   ☐ - 4 = 16   (__20__)

   The number is 20,   because   <u>20</u> - 4 = 16

   (To find the number, work backwards and do the opposite sum: 16 <u>+ 4</u> = 20)

2.   **Three times a number plus 10 is 25.**

   What is the number?   3 x ☐ + 10 = 25   (__5__)

   The number is 5,   because   3 x <u>5</u> + 10 = 25

   (To find the number, work backwards and each time do the opposite sums: 25 <u>- 10</u> = 15 <u>÷ 3</u> = 5)

STEP BY STEP

THINGS TO LOOK FOR:-

• WORK BACKWARDS AND **DO THE OPPOSITE SUM** TO WHAT IS GIVEN
• <u>ADD</u> AND <u>TAKE AWAY</u> ARE OPPOSITES
• <u>MULTIPLY</u> AND <u>DIVIDE</u> ARE OPPOSITES
• DO **WRITTEN WORKING OUT**

STEP 1:-   Write down each question in numbers using a box ☐ for the missing number.

STEP 2:-   Write down the final number given (after the '=' sign).

STEP 3:-   With this number, do the opposite sum to any ADD or SUBTRACT part of the question.

STEP 4:-   Using the answer to Step 3, do the opposite sum to any multiply or divide part of the question.

In the following questions you are asked to find the value of a certain number from some information given. Find the answer by writing down each question in numbers, using a box ☐ to stand for the certain number. If necessary, use the HINTS.

1 If I add 10 to a number the answer is 24. What is the number? (_____)

☐ + 10 = 24. Write down the final number after '=' sign and do the **opposite** sum to +10

2 A certain number plus 4 equals 12. What is the number? (_____)

☐ + ... = ...

3 When Naomi subtracts 9 from a certain number the answer is 10.
What is the number? (_____)

Write the answer down in numbers after the box: ☐ - .... = ... Then do the **opposite** sum.

4 Five times a certain number is 35. What is the number? (_____)

.... x ☐ = ... Write down the final number after the '=' sign and do the **opposite** sum to 'times 5'.

5 Half of a certain number is 12. What is the number? (_____)

'Half of' means ÷ by 2, so ☐ ÷ 2 = 12. Do the **opposite** sum to ÷ 2.

6 When 4 is subtracted from 3 times a certain number, the answer is 26.
What is the number? (_____)

3 x ☐ - 4 = 26. With '26' Do the **opposite** sum to '-4', then with this answer do the **opposite** sum to 'x3'

7 Half of a certain number added to 24 is 32. What is the number? (_____)

☐ ÷ .... + ... = 32. Do the **opposite** sum to 'add 24', then the **opposite** sum to 'half of', **in that order.**

8 Sam adds 6 to a third of a certain number and gets 18. What is the number? (_____)

6 + ☐ ÷ 3 = 18. Do the **opposite** sums to 'add 6', and then to 'a third of', **in that order.**

9 One quarter of a certain number plus 10 equals 30. What is the number? (_____)

☐ ÷ 4 + 10 = 30.

10 I get a total of 53 when I add 9 to 4 times a certain number. What is the number? (_____)

Score **10**

HOW WELL DID YOU DO?

STEP BY STEP

STEP 1:- Look at the example for a score of $\frac{7}{10}$.

STEP 2:- Now shade in the bar chart below with your score for each unit.

STEP 3:- Enter at the bottom of the page how often you got each score.

STEP 4:- Enter your most common score in the box.

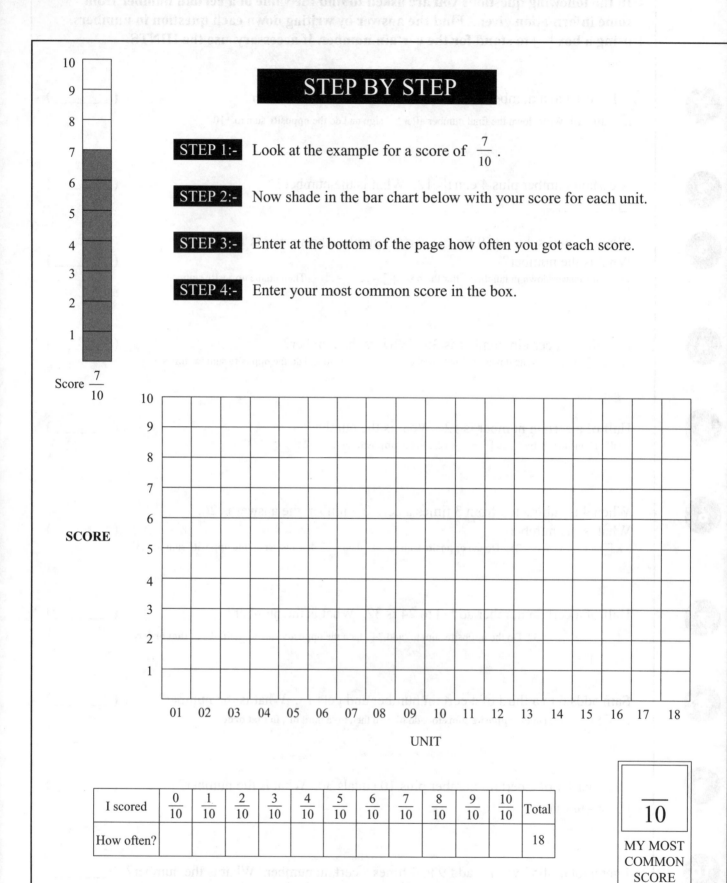

Score $\frac{7}{10}$

SCORE

UNIT

I scored	$\frac{0}{10}$	$\frac{1}{10}$	$\frac{2}{10}$	$\frac{3}{10}$	$\frac{4}{10}$	$\frac{5}{10}$	$\frac{6}{10}$	$\frac{7}{10}$	$\frac{8}{10}$	$\frac{9}{10}$	$\frac{10}{10}$	Total
How often?												18

$\overline{10}$

MY MOST COMMON SCORE

**Now you have finished this book, you are ready to start Test 01 in
LEARNING TOGETHER's Preparation for 11+ and 12+ Tests - Verbal Reasoning Book One.**

STEP BY STEP VERBAL REASONING
ANSWERS

UNIT 1
1. P
2. O
3. D
4. I
5. L
6. R
7. C
8. T
9. N
10. E

UNIT 2
1. train   rain
2. rent   even
3. chats   catch
4. mess   beams
5. daisy   solid
6. inner   angle
7. there   hotter
8. nailed   linen
9. insane   sinner
10. meant   intone

UNIT 3
1. apple, easy, hope, jet, zoo,
2. king, old, parrot, pear, young,
3. tap, ten, tin, toe, tune
4. slip, slope, stop, swab, swig
5. gannet, gap, garage, ghost, grumble,
6. exciting, exclude, excuse, execute, exit,
7. treat, treble, tree, tremble, trend
8. profess, profit, programme, prosper, protect,
9. shack, shade, shaded, shades, shake,
10. flag, flake, fleece, fleet, fleeting,

UNIT 4
1. be   I
2. last   leave
3. the(2nd)   rug
4. it   was
5. that   is
6. can   money
7. was   were
8. for   four
9. to   too
10. from   of

UNIT 5
1. JUMP
2. SOFA
3. HOUR
4. TWICE
5. LARGE
6. FORTY
7. PLANET
8. LOUNGE
9. PANTHER
10. TOMORROW

UNIT 6
1. H
2. P
3. R
4. P
5. S
6. O
7. U
8. H
9. Z
10. A

UNIT 7
1. BLACK   BOARD
2. HOUSE   WIFE
3. IN   TEND
4. POST   AGE
5. IS   LAND
6. CHILD   HOOD
7. OVER   TAKE
8. HE   AT
9. SO   ME
10. GROW   LED

UNIT 8
1. EZ
2. AV
3. JI
4. RO
5. PL
6. UJ
7. MN
8. NQ
9. TC
10. BK

UNIT 9
1. PINE
2. CLIP
3. ROLL
4. PEARL
5. ROBBER
6. PMLXG
7. LGPIY
8. CRRV
9. EHDU
10. VKDUH

LEARNING·TOGETHER.

STEP BY STEP VERBAL REASONING

UNIT 10
1. LAKE
2. TENT
3. BEAT
4. THIN
5. HARE
6. BORN
7. COST
8. SOLE
9. PINE
10. FOUL

UNIT 11
1. D
2. B
3. D
4. C
5. B
6. D
7. B
8. C
9. A
10. D

UNIT 12
1. M   AN   FORM
2. T   WE   TEAR
3. M   TIE   ZOOM
4. A   COT   FAIR
5. T   WIN   HEART
6. B   BAY   PLUMB
7. E   STAR   HOPE
8. R   BAND   CROW
9. R   EACH   PRICK
10. O   HARD   HELLO

UNIT 13
1. E
2. I
3. G
4. H
5. Y
6. T
7. K
8. P
9. L
10. W

UNIT 14
1. seat (excercise at)
2. hens (then start)
3. rest (are still)
4. fall (of all)
5. meal (some always)
6. form (For my)
7. dent (hidden this)
8. very (clever you)
9. heat (with eating)
10. wear (we are)

UNIT 15
1. AMAN (A)
2. EDDIE (E)
3. BILL (B)
4. ONE (1)
5. DIANA (D)
6. ROBERT (R)
7. ASHLEY (A)
8. BIJAY (B)
9. TWO (2)
10. NONE (0)

	A	B	C	D	E			S	R	B	A	N
Science	✓	✓										
Maths	✓	✓										
English	✓	✓										
Tennis								✓	✓	✓		
Football								✓	✓	✓		
Piano								✓	✓	✓	✓	✓
Going Abroad								✓	✓	✓	✓	✓

UNIT 16
1. WEEP
2. HEAR
3. KID
4. TREE
5. THEIR
6. WEDNESDAY
7. SEPTEMBER
8. FOOT
9. SHOAL
10. LIVE

UNIT 17
1. FOR
2. WAR
3. ALL
4. ROW
5. HOP
6. TIN
7. EVE
8. MEN
9. NOT
10. TIE

UNIT 18
1. 14
2. 8
3. 19
4. 7
5. 24
6. 10
7. 16
8. 36
9. 80
10. 11

PUBLISHED BY LEARNING TOGETHER
23 Carlston Avenue, Cultra, Co. Down BT18 0NF
Telephone/Fax: 028 9040 2086 / 028 9042 5852
www.learningtogether.co.uk email: info@learningtogether.co.uk

©Philip Kay BA